MEDICAL PRACTICE MANAGEMENT
Body of Knowledge Review

4th
Edition

ORGANIZATIONAL GOVERNANCE

VOLUME 6

MGMA
104 Inverness Terrace East
Englewood, CO 80112-5306
877.275.6462
mgma.com

Published by: Medical Group Management Association (MGMA)

Library of Congress Control Number: 2020914189

Item: 1035
ISBN: 978-1-56829-054-6

Printed in the United States of America

10 9 8 7 6 5 4 3 2 1

Body of Knowledge Review Series, 4th Edition

VOLUME 1: Operations Management

VOLUME 2: Financial Management

VOLUME 3: Human Resource Management

VOLUME 4: Transformative Healthcare Delivery

VOLUME 5: Risk and Compliance Management

VOLUME 6: Organizational Governance

Acknowledgments

Thank you to the members of the ACMPE Certification Commission who guided the 2019-20 update to the Body of Knowledge for Medical Practice Management:

Tracy Bird, FACMPE, CPC, CPMA, CEMC, CPC-I
David Taylor, FACMPE, FACHE
Deborah Hudson, FACMPE
Mona Millner, MHA, NHA, FACHE, FACMPE, FHFMA, FACHCA
Andrew Smith, MHA, FACMPE
Kristina Owens, MSBA, FACMPE

Further thanks to the following MGMA members who lent their expertise as subject matter experts to update the Body of Knowledge framework and content development as members of the ACMPE Body of Knowledge Oversight Committee:

Bonnie Bina, MS, MA, FACMPE
Lee Ann Webster, MA, CPA, FACMPE
Sandra Deleon, FACHE, CMPE, MSHA, MSW
Dennis Walker, CMPE, FACHE
Douglas Blackard, MHA, MS, CMPE
Eric Weaver, FACMPE, FHIMSS, FACHE
Sean Marshall, MSC, CMPE
Leland Tong, CMPE
Linda Clark, FACMPE
Amber McKinney, FACMPE
Frank Ford, MBA, MHS, FACMPE
Jeffrey Rydburg, CMPE
Cinderella Tollefsen, MBA, FACMPE
Miku Sodhi, MBBS, MD, MHA, PCMH-CCE, FACMPE
Rosalba Lozano, MBA, LSSGB, FACMPE
Andrew Smith, MHA, FACMPE
Robert Karam, BS, BSN, MA
Barbara Daniels, FACMPE
Dickson Capps, FACMPE, FACHE, FASHE, LMASCE
Dan Cole, CMPE

A special thank you is also extended to the MGMA staff and the following writers and editors for their contributions:

Penny M. Crow, MS, SHRM-SCP, RHIA *(Writer)*
Sharon Z. Ginchansky, MAOM *(Writer)*
Jim Goldmann, MHA *(Writer)*
M. Christine Kalish, MBA, CMPE *(Writer)*
Kelly Kagamas Tomkies *(Writer and Editor)*
Melissa L. Weber, MA *(Editor)*

Contents

Updates to information in this volume are likely to be made as changes in the healthcare industry occur. Keep up with all updates to the *Body of Knowledge Review Series, 4th Edition* at mgma.com/BOKupdates.

Introduction

Business executives in all industries are responsible for providing broad organizational leadership and for defining and achieving corporate goals. Healthcare executives are no exception.

Among other duties, a healthcare executive's key responsibilities may include:

- Defining the mission, vision, and values of the organization
- Identifying and establishing the most appropriate legal model for reaching organizational goals
- Creating a robust corporate culture
- Providing direction for the overall leadership of the organization

Demonstrating knowledge and skills in fulfilling theses duties is essential for developing healthcare leadership expertise, and also for meeting the requirements for achieving Fellowship status as outlined by the Medical Group Management Association (MGMA).

This volume is a blueprint designed by MGMA Fellows and members who have hands-on healthcare practice leadership experience. It provides detailed explanations of MGMA expectations, as well as the information Fellow candidates need to meet those expectations.

As a healthcare executive, you should have knowledge of:

- The definition of corporate culture, the different types of corporate culture, and how to identify and change an existing culture

- The importance of an organization's vision, mission, and values statement in creating and supporting an organization's culture
- Corporate structure options for healthcare organizations, and the pros and cons of each type of structure
- How to determine the most appropriate leadership model for the organization
- Healthcare organizations' obligation to comply with all governmental regulations and statutes

You should also be able to demonstrate skills in the following:

- Participating in the development of the organization's mission, vision, and value statements and how to use them in creating a robust corporate culture
- Ensuring that the organization's vision, mission, and values are reflected in the way it operates
- Selecting the most appropriate legal corporate structure
- Implementing optimal governance and structures that provide corporate leadership
- Creating policies, procedures, and systems to ensure the organization's compliance with governmental regulations and statutes
- Updating the organization's documents, policies, and procedures as required and necessary to reflect changes in the internal or external environment or regulatory changes

This volume's three chapters provide more details of these expectations related to organizational culture, legal structure, and governance, as well as practical guidance for establishing each one.

Chapter 1

Corporate Mission, Vision, and Values

The quality of an organization's culture is a key determinant of its success or failure. A strong, positive culture can lead to a medical practice's success, while a dysfunctional or undefined culture can make it difficult or impossible for the practice to achieve its goals.

Culture is the foundation of corporate identity. Culture reflects the practice's most closely held values and beliefs, guides day-to-day decision making, and governs how decisions are implemented.

The importance of culture is not theoretical. Many daily operational challenges can be traced to a dysfunctional or poorly defined corporate culture. When the culture, and its underlying components of vision, mission, and values, are unclear, the healthcare executive cannot reliably measure whether the organization is moving closer to or further from its goals. This ambiguity can permeate all levels of an organization, affect the staffs' confidence and cause questions about the direction the organization is going, and lead to the perception that the organization is under poor leadership.

Many of the problems confronting healthcare practices can be traced to an inability to analyze, evaluate, and shape organizational cultures.

When trying to implement new strategies or a strategic plan, healthcare executives will often discover that their strategies will

1

fail if they are implementing programs that are inconsistent with the organization's culture.

Definition and Importance of Culture

One widely accepted definition of culture is "the way things are done around here."[1] Peter Drucker, renowned management theorist and educator, expanded this definition when he wrote that "Culture is an organization's self-sustaining patterns of behaving, feeling, thinking and believing."[2] Drucker's definition shows that culture can determine an organization's self-image, its external image, and the way it operates. In other words, just about everything related to an organization is defined by its culture.

Drucker emphasized the centrality of culture when he wrote that "Culture eats strategy for breakfast." Drucker's comment implies that the best business plans and strategies will fail if they are not supported by a robust and enthusiastic culture.

In his book *Organizational Culture and Leadership,*[3] Edward Schein presents five guidelines for understanding corporate culture:

1. Do not oversimplify culture or confuse it with climate, values, or corporate philosophy. Culture underlies, supports, and largely determines these other factors of an organization. Trying to change values or climate without understanding how they will impact corporate culture may not produce the desired results.

2. Do not label culture as solely a human resource aspect of an organization, affecting only its human side. The impact of culture goes far beyond the human side of the organization to affect and influence its basic mission, goals, and how it functions every day.

3. Do not assume that practice leadership can manipulate culture in the same way leaders might seek to control other aspects of the organization. Culture, because it is largely determined and controlled by the members

of the organization and not the healthcare executive, is different. Culture may end up controlling the leader rather than the other way around.

4. Do not assume there is a "right" or "wrong" culture, or that one type of culture is necessarily superior to another. Cultural fit is organization-specific, and one type of culture may better serve the practice's mission and strategic goals than others.

5. Do not assume that all the aspects of organizational culture are important or will have a major effect on how it functions. Some elements of an organization's culture may have little effect on its function. The healthcare executive must distinguish between which elements are important and impact how the organization functions, and which elements have little impact.

In addition, McKinsey and Company[4] defined four reasons that corporate culture matters:

1. Culture correlates with performance. Organizations that have a positive, performance-driven culture are consistently more successful than organizations that do not.

2. Culture is unique to every organization, cannot be readily duplicated by competitors, and is essential for the practice to differentiate itself in the market.

3. Organizations that have performance-driven cultures adapt more successfully to environmental changes and enjoy a competitive advantage over organizations that are resistant to change.

4. Unhealthy cultures can lead to underperformance or worse. Over time, not only do unhealthy cultures foster lackluster performance, but they can also prevent an organization from achieving its goals.

Identifying a practice's corporate culture and transforming that culture when necessary require advanced skills on the part of the healthcare executive that can only be developed with time and experience.

Attempting to change an existing culture without having the necessary skills and experience can damage the practice, impair its ability to achieve its goals, and create the perception of inadequate executive leadership.

The Components of Culture: Mission, Vision, and Values

The components essential for building a corporate culture are mission, vision, values. Another important component for healthcare practices is the commitment to creating a high reliability and zero harm organization. A high reliability company is one in which the organization maintains extraordinarily high levels of quality and safety over long periods of time with no or extremely few adverse or harmful events, despite operating in hazardous conditions. A zero harm organization in the healthcare industry has "zero complications of care, zero falls, zero infections, zero missed opportunities for providing effective care, zero overuse and even zero lost revenue. In other words, zero harm of any kind."[5]

In combination, all of these components can create a highly productive culture that motivates and rewards employees to meet corporate goals while delivering the highest possible levels of safety and quality patient care.

An important cultural component that sometimes can be overlooked is the organization's need to understand and be continually in compliance with all federal and state regulations. While sometimes seen as bothersome in the healthcare industry, these regulatory requirements are designed to encourage the delivery of only medically necessary patient care in a financially and legally responsible way. Failure to comply at all times with governmental regulations can result in dire financial, legal, reputational, and operational consequences, up to and including federal investigation, heavy fines, and expulsion from the Medicare and Medicaid programs.

The governing body and healthcare executive are responsible for creating, implementing, and maintaining a compliance-driven culture and for ensuring that this culture is understood and adopted throughout the medical practice.

Developing and personally communicating the organization's corporate mission, vision, and values statements are critical responsibilities for the healthcare executive and should never be delegated to someone who has a lower-level role in leadership. Staff buy-in of the corporate mission, vision, and values statements can be predicated on their belief that the healthcare executive helped to develop them, fully understands them, and completely supports them.

Figure 1.1[6] defines mission, vision, and values, and shows how they interact to create and provide on-going support of corporate culture.

Figure 1.1

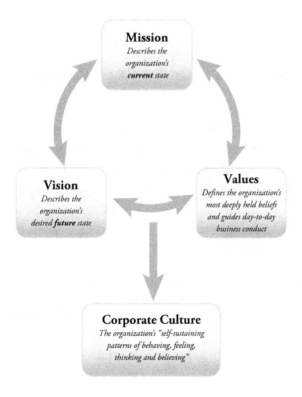

Mission
Describes the organization's current state

Vision
Describes the organization's desired future state

Values
Defines the organization's most deeply held beliefs and guides day-to-day business conduct

Corporate Culture
The organization's "self-sustaining patterns of behaving, feeling, thinking and believing"

As synergy develops across these components, they reinforce one another over time and result in an organizational culture that becomes either increasingly effective or increasingly dysfunctional. As the illustration shows, this dynamic reinforces the importance of establishing and maintaining a positive culture. Maintaining a positive culture is much easier than repairing a negative one.

Mission Statement Definition and Development

The mission statement explains why an organization exists, describes the services it provides, who its customers are, and how services will be delivered.

From a leadership perspective, an effective mission statement:

- Outlines the organization's approach for fulfilling its purpose
- Creates staff loyalty and motivates them by explaining the organization's purpose and demonstrating the leadership's commitment to fulfilling it
- Provides healthcare executives a way to measure whether the organization is moving closer to or further from its goals

Forbes magazine emphasizes the organizational value of increasing employee engagement by noting that "Mission-driven workers are 54 percent more likely to stay for five years at a company and 30 percent more likely to grow into high performers."[7] Better employee retention makes it easier to achieve corporate goals, in part because it also reduces the company's expenses related to turnover such as staff recruitment, orientation, and training.

The most effective corporate mission statements are:

- Succinct and sufficiently brief to be printed on the back of a business card
- Memorable and easy for practice staff to remember and recite

- Plainly written and easy to understand (an overly long or complex statement can limit understanding and reduce organization-wide buy in)
- Organization-specific and describe the practice's purpose in a unique and non-generic way
- Realistic and credible; the mission statement is not an aspirational document; its purpose is to define why the organization exists, the services it provides, and who it serves

When the healthcare executive is establishing the practice's corporate mission, it is important to include input from stakeholders at all organizational levels, including the governing body (board of directors), providers, the executive leadership team, managers, and staff. Broad-based stakeholder participation in the development process improves the quality, organizational understanding, and buy-in of the corporate mission statement.

Because group medical practices often have similar mission statements, however, the mission statement alone cannot effectively distinguish one practice from another in a competitive environment.

Market differentiation depends on how quickly the practice perceives and effectively responds to changes in the market.

Practices that recognize changes in their environment and effectively adjust to those changes have a significant competitive advantage over those that do not. Skillful change management can make the difference between successful group practices and those that are left behind.

Vision Statement Definition and Development

The vision statement defines the organization's aspirations for the future. It is forward-facing and optimistic by design and should foster employee commitment by painting a picture of what the organization wants to accomplish in the future.

An effective vision statement also builds staff confidence in the organization by showing that the corporate mission will remain in place

7

as the organization moves into the future. Basing the vision statement on the organization's mission lets staff know that no matter what the future holds, the organization will remain true to its purpose as it pursues its vision.

Best medical practice vision statements are:

1. Future-oriented. The vision statement is not what the company is doing today, but rather sets a future objective or goal for where the company hopes to go.

2. Concise. This is not the place to fill a document with elaborate statements. The vision statement should be simple, easy to read, and cut to the chase so that it can be easily remembered and spoken accurately.

3. Reflective of a company's culture and core values.

4. Optimistic, inspirational, and paint a bright picture of the future that rallies all staff members and employees to work toward a common goal.

5. Challenging. Corporate vision is aspirational and should take a bold view when setting future goals.

6. Realistic, attainable, and seen as credible to leadership and staff. While the vision should not be too easy to achieve, it also should not be so unrealistic that employees feel it will be impossible to achieve, and so ignore it.

7. Clear. A good rule of thumb for clarity is to focus on one primary goal, rather than trying to fill the document with several scattered ideas. One clear objective is also easier to focus on and achieve.

8. Tied to the corporate mission and shows that the practice's purpose will remain unchanged as the organization moves into the future.

9. Stable. The vision statement should neither be driven by market forces or developments nor require changes in the organization's corporate mission.

10. General in nature. The vision statement is not a strategic plan with specific steps for achieving success. It should be broad enough to capture the organization's overall interests and future direction. To be credible, the vision statement should define organizational aspirations for the near- to mid-term. A statement that describes a too-distant future often is seen as unrealistic and will fail to motivate or inspire employees.

Values Statement Definition and Development

A corporate values statement defines the organization's most deeply held beliefs that form the foundation of its corporate identity. While the corporate mission defines *what* the organization is and its purpose, values represent *how* the organization will endeavor to achieve that mission on a daily basis.

Corporate values underlie daily decision-making and determine how those decisions are implemented. Values are critical in helping practice leaders endeavor to make the right choices, at the right time. Paying attention to organizational values also ensures that the practice's decision-making remains internally consistent through good times and bad.

Studies show that when organizational values give people a sense of meaning in their work, it is not only good for employees, it is essential for building a healthy organization that is highly functional and competitive.

Effective values statements are:

1. Unique to each organization and reflect how employees think and feel about the organization at the moment.

2. Central to developing a high-performance culture. It is impossible to develop a high performing culture without values that define and support that behavior.

3. Collaborative in nature and should include input from staff at all levels of the organization.

9

4. More discovered than created; in other words, while corporate values can and should be deliberately defined, they ultimately depend more on how employees understand and practice them on a daily basis.

5. Not just a behavior, but also a mindset.

Values reflect not only how employees do their work on a daily basis, but also—and perhaps most importantly—how they think and feel about their work while they're doing it. Understanding how employees feel about what they do is the primary way healthcare executives gain an understanding of whether employees are motivated and can be highly productive, or disengaged from the work and less likely to meet practice goals. Overlooking the cognitive aspect of employee behavior makes it difficult to understand how specific values developed and why employees might be resistant to change.

Influencing corporate values is challenging, time-consuming, and requires healthcare executives to lead by example, consistently modeling the behaviors they desire in others at the practice every day. Practice staff members will not change their behavior until they believe practice leaders believe the corporate values they espouse and are completely committed to putting them in place.

High-Reliability and Zero-Harm Organization

An important component of corporate culture, and one that should be explicitly reflected in the mission statement, is the practice's commitment to creating a "high-reliability" and "zero-harm" organization.

A high-reliability organization is supported by a culture of "collective mindfulness where workers look for, report, and address small problems or unsafe conditions when they are easy to fix, and long before they pose a major hazard."[8] High-reliability cultures also encourage staff to do the analysis, critical thinking, and performance reporting required to continuously improve patient care systems, processes, and outcomes.

Reason and Hobbs[9] describe a high-reliability organization as not only having a strong commitment to safety, but also as ". . . being learning organizations. Learning organizations value errors and close calls which they regard as free lessons that lead to the identification and resolution of weaknesses in the systems and structures designed by the organization to prevent harm."

The drive to establish high-reliability organizations began with The Institute of Medicine's 2000 report, *To Err is Human*,[10] which moved patient safety to the forefront of healthcare leaders' priorities. The prioritization of patient safety has resulted in remarkable improvements in quality of care, such as the decline in incidences of hospital-acquired illnesses and reductions in unnecessary procedures and other progress.

Establishing a high-reliability organization requires healthcare executive and board commitment to make patient safety the organization's number one goal. This also ensures that high reliability is reflected in the organization's culture. The organization is seen as valuing open and honest communication about ways to improve patient care systems and outcomes.

Practices should also aim to become zero-harm organizations. Even though no group practice can deliver perfect, completely error-free care, striving to achieve zero harm is an aspirational goal that should be an important component of culture. The commitment to becoming a zero-harm organization demonstrates the practice's dedication to continuously providing the highest possible levels of safe and quality patient care.

Examples of Group Practice Mission, Vision, and Values Statements

Here are some examples of various healthcare organizations' mission, vision, and values statements. Notice that these statements are consistent with best practices described earlier in this chapter. Each organization's statements are succinct, easy to understand, organization-specific, realistic, and aspirational. These statements are readily available for the general public to read on the organizations' websites.

Mayo Clinic

- Mission: To inspire hope and contribute to health and well-being by providing the best care to every patient through integrated clinical practice, education and research.
- Vision: Mayo Clinic will provide an unparalleled experience as the most trusted partner for health care.
- Values: These values guide Mayo Clinic's mission:
  - o Primary value: The needs of the patient come first.
  - o Respect: Treat everyone in our diverse community, including patients, their families and colleagues, with dignity.
  - o Integrity: Adhere to the highest standards of professionalism, ethics and personal responsibility, worthy of the trust our patients place in us.
  - o Compassion: Provide the best care, treating patients and family members with sensitivity and empathy.
  - o Healing: Inspire hope and nurture the well-being of the whole person, respecting physical, emotional, and spiritual needs.
  - o Teamwork: Value the contributions of all, blending the skills of individual staff members in unsurpassed collaboration.
  - o Innovation: Infuse and energize the organization, enhancing the lives of those we serve, through the creative ideas and unique talents of each employee.
  - o Excellence: Deliver the best outcomes and highest quality service through the dedicated effort of every team member.
  - o Stewardship: Sustain and reinvest in our mission and extended communities by wisely managing our human, natural, and material resources.

Kaiser Permanente

- Mission: Kaiser Permanente exists to provide high-quality, affordable healthcare services and to improve the health of our members and the communities we serve.
- Vision: We understand that you want the best care possible for yourself and your loved ones, and our mission is to provide this high-quality care. We continuously work to live up to your expectations, and we strive to improve our care. Improved care by Kaiser Permanente translates into improved health for the members we serve, making high-quality care a goal we all want to achieve.
- Our vision at Kaiser Permanente is to be a leader in total health by making lives better.
- Values: In carrying out our mission and goals, we maintain core values of respect, scientific discipline, integrity, pioneering spirit, and stewardship.

Cleveland Clinic

- Mission: To provide better care of the sick, investigation in their problems, and further education of those who serve.
- Vision: Our vision for the Cleveland Clinic is to be the best place for care anywhere and the best place to work in health care.
- Values: Quality and Safety: We ensure the highest standards and excellent outcomes through effective interactions, decision-making, and actions.
- Empathy: We imagine what another person is going through, work to alleviate suffering, and create joy whenever possible.
- Inclusion: We intentionally create an environment of compassionate belonging where all are valued and respected.
- Integrity: We adhere to high moral principles and professional standards by a commitment to honesty, confidentiality, trust, respect, and transparency.

- Teamwork: We work together to ensure the best possible care, safety, and well-being of our patients and fellow caregivers.
- Innovation: We drive small and large changes to transform health care everywhere.

Culture Types and Characteristics

Robert E. Quinn and Kim S. Cameron of the University of Michigan[11] categorize corporate culture into four types: adhocracy, clan, hierarchy, and market.

Adhocracy culture is externally focused, adept at recognizing and adapting to change, and is characterized by high levels of innovation, experimentation, disruption, and risk-taking. This cultural type is most often seen in fast-paced, entrepreneurial organizations that demand a high level of flexibility in responding to market changes. It is common among tech companies that must strive to stay ahead of the competition when it comes to new products. In general, the adhocracy culture is usually appropriate or commonly used in medical practices.

Clan culture relies on personal relationships, collaboration, team building, employee engagement, human resources training and development, mentoring, and coaching to achieve its goals. This cultural type is most often seen in "high touch," people-oriented organizations where human resources are the most important asset. Most medical group practices' cultures are clan-oriented.

Hierarchy cultures emphasize efficiency, standardized processes, tight cost control, continual performance improvement, high levels of technical expertise, and advanced problem-solving. This cultural type is often seen in highly structured, bureaucratic organizations that must produce consistently high quality products and outcomes to compete in a competitive market. Many medical practice cultures incorporate aspects of the hierarchy culture.

Market cultures are hard-driving and focused on delivering high shareholder value, competing for capital and market share, fast decision making, and the consistent delivery of on-time results. Market cultures break down barriers and have directive and commanding leadership styles. This culture is best suited for a marketing-and-sales-oriented organization responsible for getting products and services to market. Many medical practice cultures include elements of a market culture when they are provider-owned and focused on increasing and delivering shareholder value.

It is unusual for an organization to have a "pure" culture, in other words, one that is reflective of just one of these four types. Most organizations, including medical practices, are a mixture of types, combining elements from each type of culture to meet organization-specific needs. For example, smaller, single specialty practices may draw most heavily on clan culture, while those that are larger and more complex may include elements of adhocracy, clan, and hierarchy cultures.

There are several factors that influence the design and development of a practice's corporate culture, including who owns the practice, levels of organizational complexity, range of services provided, patient population, risk tolerance, and the organization's values.

Organizational Size and Complexity

Larger, more complex practices (e.g., those that are structured as S or C corporations) that offer a broader range of services typically have cultures that incorporate elements of multiple culture types, including adhocracy, clan, and hierarchy.

While these organizations may have an overarching culture, subsets of other culture types can develop in departments that are functionally distinct and require varying levels of expertise and problem solving.

For example, a practice offering multi-specialty inpatient and outpatient services and procedures across multiple locations can develop cultural subsets individually based on the range of services provided and the different patients that are served.

Smaller, less complex practices (e.g., sole proprietorships, or smaller professional associations or corporations) typically rely on the clan type of culture. In this type of culture, the quality of relationships and degree of collaboration among team members will determine the organization's success.

The coexistence of both of these cultural types in one organization, especially at the leadership level, can generate internal conflict as leaders try to balance the drive for increased profitability with the need to provide high quality care as efficiently as possible. Well-defined and accepted corporate values can aid in the reconciliation of these types of internal conflicts.

Unfortunately, not all practices have, or consistently adhere to, well-defined corporate values. This can cause the organization to sway between competing goals and result in irrational decision making based on the dominant priority of the moment. This situation can erode employee confidence in the organization, as well as its purpose and mission, and decrease staff commitment and motivation to achieve corporate goals.

Ownership

Practices that are owned by the providers as shareholders develop a culture based on the owners' priorities, goals, and values. Owners focused on improving shareholder value through increased profitability tend to be more risk tolerant and control-oriented. They foster cultures closely tied to the hierarchy and market types.

Shareholder-owned practices with a greater focus on internal and external relationships and the provision of patient care tend to be more risk averse and rely more heavily on the clan culture type. They may also include elements of the hierarchy type.

Practices that have a more corporate structure tend to have a relatively low risk tolerance, depend on well-defined management structures and tight process controls, and develop cultures most closely tied to the hierarchy and market types.

Practices owned by or affiliated with external provider-based or corporate entities tend to be risk averse, dependent on external leadership and management, have limited control over provider income, and share practice net profit with the "parent" organization. These organizations are often required to adopt at least some elements of the larger organization's culture and tend to develop a hierarchy culture to ensure that internal operations meet external corporate goals. They may also adopt the elements of a clan culture that are needed to successfully manage relationships with external owners.

Conclusion

A healthy culture is essential for any highly functioning medical practice. These cultures require thoughtfully developed statements of corporate mission, vision, and values. Without these components, organizational culture will develop organically, which may result in unpredictable and inconsistent performance. Defining and communicating the organization's corporate mission, vision, and values are critical to the success of the organization, and an important responsibility of the healthcare executive.

Notes

1. Kennedy, Allan and Terrence Deal. *Corporate Cultures: The Rites and Rituals of Corporate Life*, Cambridge: Perseus Books Group, 2000.

2. Drucker, Peter, The Leader to Leader Institute. *The Five Most Important Questions You Will Ever Ask About Your Organization*, San Francisco: Jossey-Bass Publishing, 2008.

3. Schein, Edward. *Organizational Culture and Leadership*, Hoboken: John Wiley & Sons, Inc., 2017.

4. Dewar, Carolyn and Reed Doucette. "Culture: 4 keys to why it matters," http://mckinsey.com/business-functions/organization/our-insights/the-organization-blog/culture-4-keys-to-why-it-matters, March 27, 2018.

5. Joint Commission, "Leading the Way to Zero: Did You Know," http://jointcommission.org, 2000.

6. Kolomiyets, Tetyana, "Organizational culture and its mission, vision and values," *UNECE Statistics Wikis*, last modified April 23, 2020, https://statswiki.unece.org/display/SCFP/Organizational+culture+and+its+mission%2C+vision+and+values;

Jaruzelski, Barry, John Lehr, and Richard Holman, "The Global Innovation 1000: Why Culture is Key," *strategy+business*, Winter 2011, https://strategy-business.com/article/11404?gko=62080.

7. Craig, William, "The Importance of Having a Mission-Driven Company," *Forbes*, May 15, 2018.

8. Chassin, Mark R. and Jerod M. Loeb, "High-Reliability Health Care: Getting There from Here," *The Milbank Quarterly*, September 13, 2013.

9. Reason, James and Alan Hobbs, *Managing Maintenance Error: A Practical Guide*, Boca Raton: CRC Press, 2003.

10. Kohn, Linda, Janet Corrigan, and Molla S. Donaldson, *To Err is Human: Building a Safer Health System*, Washington D.C.: National Academies Press, 2000.

11. Quinn, Robert and Kim Cameron, *Diagnosing and Changing Organizational Culture: Based on the Competing Values Framework*, San Francisco: Jossey-Bass Publishing, 2011.

Chapter 2

Corporate Legal Structure

Understanding the possible business structures available to medical practices and selecting the one that is most appropriate are essential skills for healthcare executives. Each business structure has specific legal, risk, and tax implications that can either serve the practice's needs or compromise them. Medical practice governing bodies and leaders often do not understand the features and potential impacts of different legal models, nor do they recognize how each may or may not advance corporate goals. A skilled healthcare executive must understand the types of business structures available, as well as the advantages and disadvantages of each one. Healthcare executives must be able to explain these structures to board members and other senior practice leaders.

Choosing the best model depends on the legal risks and tax profile that best fit the practice's mission and goals.

Understanding Corporate Business Structure

Before choosing the best business structure for the practice, the healthcare executive must clearly understand why the organization exists, what it wants to accomplish in the future, and the values it will practice getting there. This information should be available in the corporate mission, vision, and values statements. Once the healthcare executive recommends a business structure, it should be approved by

19

the practice's governing body to ensure it will help the organization meet its goals.

The medical practice's business structure determines the tax liability exposure, the degree of flexibility in fulfilling corporate strategy, and helps to define physician compensation options. Therefore, the board and the healthcare executive should carefully define practice expectations in all of these areas.

Defining the practice's liability tolerance might appear straightforward. All practices want the lowest possible level of risk. However, this decision is more nuanced than it may appear because while certain legal models provide extensive risk protection, they also can narrow the options practices will have for growing and responding to changes in their markets.

For example, there are important differences across S corporations, C corporations, and limited liability partnerships and corporations (LLCs) that specify how taxes, net income, and retained earnings are recorded, and how or whether the income and earnings may be distributed as physician compensation. In addition, certain legal structures can simplify the acquisition of assets for growth, increase access to capital, and maximize practice value if the practice is considering being sold to or acquired by another company.

Some governing boards are willing to accept some increased liability exposure to preserve greater flexibility in achieving corporate strategic goals.

While the healthcare executive is responsible for recommending to the board the business structure that is the best fit, this process can be complex and require specialized legal and tax expertise unavailable within the organization. Outside expert advice is often worth the cost because it is less expensive to choose the right legal model today than to correct an inappropriate choice in the future.

Understanding Business Structures

Most medical groups in the United States use one of the following models for establishing their business structure:

- Sole proprietorship
- Professional corporation (PC) or professional association (PA)
- Professional limited liability partnership (PLLP)
- Professional limited liability company (PLLC)

State laws define the available legal structures, as well as their benefits and requirements. Medical practices are typically organized and operated using a separate legal entity (e.g., a separately incorporated professional corporation) to protect personal assets of the practice owners from practice-related liabilities.

Few medical practices use either the general or limited partnership form of legal structure, mostly because these legal structures do not provide sufficient liability protection and can create significant tax disadvantages compared with other models.

From a tax perspective, the Federal Internal Revenue Code and statutes define the tax implications of each business structure.

For example, a PC is normally subject to a 35 percent federal tax rate on corporate earnings. However, the federal tax code permits a PC to be taxed at the same rates as a C corporation. C corporations are taxed at 15 percent to 34 percent of their first $100,000 in earnings, after deducting any practice losses, deductions, and credits from income. Shareholders then pay personal income taxes on the dividends. While this model does reduce the practice's federal tax rate, it exposes shareholders to double taxation by paying taxes on both corporate and personal earnings.

Rather than adopt C corporation status, a practice with fewer than 100 shareholders can elect to become an S corporation. In an S corporation, the practice can enjoy the liability protection of incorporation while being taxed as a partnership. Because no federal income tax is levied at the corporate level, the corporation can pass income directly to shareholders, who only pay personal taxes on their earnings. As a result, the S corporation model prevents the double taxation of both the PC and C corporation legal models.

Before settling on the business structure, practice leaders should always obtain professional legal and tax advice.

Descriptions, Advantages, and Disadvantages to Business Structures

As mentioned, the most common business structures are sole proprietorships, professional and business corporations, professional limited liability partnerships, and professional limited liability companies. The next section discusses each of these, along with its advantages and disadvantages. You can find more information about these business types in Chapter 6 of the *Operations Management* volume.

Sole Proprietorships

A medical practice with a single physician owner that is not established as a separate legal entity is considered a sole proprietorship. In this structure, the assets of the individual physician and the medical practice are not separate, so the physician is not protected from any liability resulting from practice activities as he or she would be in a PC or similar structure. In other words, if the practice is unable to pay all of its debts and declares bankruptcy, the physician's personal funds would be included in the assets.

It is important to note that a solo practice is not the same thing legally as a sole proprietorship. A sole proprietorship is a formal legal structure, while a solo practice is not. A solo practice may be organized as a sole proprietorship, a PC, or similar legal structure that is owned by a single physician. Under these business structures, the physician can work in a solo practice format while receiving the liability protection of a corporation.

The advantages of a sole proprietorship include:

- Control: The physician-owner has total control over money and decisions because there are no partners or shareholders.
- Flexibility: A sole proprietorship is relatively easy to set up and requires no separate tax filing.

The disadvantages of a sole proprietorship include:

- There is no history for lending purposes. It can be difficult for a new medical practice to borrow funds without collateral or a history of borrowing.
- Backup may not be available. Another provider may not be readily available to provide coverage when the physician is unavailable.
- There is no liability protection. Because a sole proprietorship is not a separate legal entity, the owner is personally responsible for all practice liabilities.
- The sole proprietor has full responsibility for practice management. In addition to providing patient care, the owner is responsible for all of the practice's financial and operational decisions.

While the majority of medical practices choose one of the four structures discussed, some choose to operate as a nonprofit organization or a nonprofit department in a larger organization. Nonprofit organizations are given 501(c)(3) tax status. Nonprofit organizations, by definition, are not legally permitted to accumulate profits. Instead, they are required to reinvest any profits they earn into the organization, facilities, or mission.

The advantages of being a nonprofit organization include:

- Exemption from paying income taxes
- Exemption from paying property taxes
- Other tax advantages can vary from state to state

The disadvantages of being a nonprofit organization include:

- Reliance on donors or on grants for funding
- Potential reliance on local community for support and funding
- Limitations on amount of funds that can be invested in financial vehicles before nonprofit status is compromised

Professional and Business Corporations

A professional corporation (PC), is a distinct legal entity that exists separate from its owners. These types of organizations have four characteristics:

1. Limited liability

2. Continuity of existence

3. Transferability of ownership

4. Centralized management

A PC is a legal entity separate from its owners for liability protection and tax advantage purposes. A PC is generally subject to the same basic requirements and rules as any other business corporation, except that only licensed professionals may own or share an interest in it. Non-providers can neither own nor invest in a PC. In addition, PC ownership can be transferred only to another licensed professional.

A business corporation is also a separate legal entity that limits the liability of its owners. Unlike a PC, however, a business corporation allows outside investors as well as ownership by non-physicians. While this legal structure shares most of the benefits of a PC (except taxation), this model is seldom used for medical practices because licensing laws in many states restrict medical practice ownership to licensed physicians.

The advantages of a corporate legal structure include:

- Limited liability. Shareholders are not responsible for corporate debt or practice-related liabilities.
- Additional tax deductions. Because the corporation pays employee and provider benefits, such as health and life insurance, those costs are tax deductible corporate expenses.
- Transferability. Ownership can be sold or transferred to another medically licensed person or entity.

The disadvantages of corporations include:

- Shareholders are double-taxed, first on corporate net income and again on personal income. Many practices can avoid this by organizing as an S corporation.
- Corporations require more complex governance and management structures with detailed reporting and documentation obligations.
- Corporations are required to have formal governance boards and typically also have very structured management models.

Professional Limited Liability Partnerships and Professional Limited Liability Companies

PLLPs and PLLCs provide different levels of legal protection or limited liability to the organization's owners. Both structures allow the profits from the limited liability partnership (LLP) or limited liability company (LLC) to be taxed as partnerships. This means there is no potential for double taxation of entity profits, as in the case of the C corporation model.

The procedure for setting up these or other forms of organizations is defined by state law, although most require the filing of articles of organization or similar shareholder documents.

Advantages of LLCs and LLPs:

- Limited personal liability. Shareholders are not responsible for corporate debt or practice-related liabilities.
- The medical practice is treated as a partnership for tax purposes, so income and losses are passed directly to the owners and are not subject to double taxation.

Disadvantages of LLCs and LLPs are:

- More complex governance
- Physicians are not employees. Physicians generally are not employees of PLLPs or PLLCs, rendering them ineligible for benefits available in a PC or similar structure.

- Different financial management. Both entities require financial management practices somewhat different from those found in the more common PC form.
- Variable state laws. Not every state allows medical practices to use a PLLP or PLLC model.

Organizational Governance

The form of governance a medical practice chooses depends, like so many other aspects discussed in this volume, on the practice's mission, vision, values, and goals. In this section of the chapter, you will read about the environmental forces shaping an organization, the governing board and its responsibilities, the executive officer and their responsibilities, and corporate record-keeping.

Environmental Forces

Most organizations, including medical practices, are open systems. This means that operations are impacted by environmental factors, including government regulations, as well as social and market changes. All of these can have a direct impact on how a medical practice operates, as well as the cost of operations. For example, when HIPAA was first enacted, healthcare providers had to make several changes to the way they operated, from providing written notices and posting signs advising patients of their right to privacy, to training employees about all of the HIPAA regulations. A practice's organizational governance can be impacted by these forces as well. For example, practices had to designate staff members to ensure HIPAA compliance, and leaders were responsible for ensuring oversight.

Organizational governance also must be community-focused when it comes to strategic management. Medical practices exist to meet the healthcare needs of the community, and each community has its own unique needs. Healthcare executives must keep those needs in mind when structuring governance of the practice.

Continuous improvement may also impact how a practice is governed and structured. As the practice engages in continuous improvement, changes may be needed in who makes decisions, for example. Continuous improvement may also lead to streamlining processes and removing some hierarchies of leadership.

Another environmental factor that impacts how a practice is governed is the scale of both the healthcare needs of the community, and the scale of the practice itself. Smaller practices or those focused on specialized care may require fewer managers, while large-scale operations may require more in order to meet patient and employee needs.

Customer or patient motivation may also impact practice strategies. If patients are highly motivated it means they usually participate more in their care and may ask for or require additional services. This may mean the practice needs additional providers or managers. Board member motivation will also impact governance. Board member focus and priorities will have a direct impact on how the practice is governed.

The Governing Board

Most healthcare organizations, both large and small, seek to establish a governing board whose purpose is to ensure the organization has the tools and support necessary to carry out its mission. The governing board also provides oversight to ensure the practice or organization is providing quality medical care and meeting its goals.

The governing board also serves these functions:

- Appoints the chief executive
- Helps to establish the practice's mission and values
- Approves long-range plans and the annual budget
- Ensures quality of medical care
- Monitors performance against plans and budgets
- Reviews resource distribution

Other responsibilities of the board may include:

- Providing and monitoring institutional goals
- Interacting with other leaders in the community

- Assessing and controlling quality
- Implementing self-assessment and professional development recommendations
- Monitoring performance

Every potential member of the board needs to understand his or her role and the expectations of the job. For example, a prospective board member might read a job description similar to the sample shown in Exhibit 2.1.

In medical groups, most members of the board are physicians. Because their duty is to the group as a whole, they must put their own interests or the interests of their specialty aside and make the needs of the entire group their priority.

Board Membership and Criteria

In most cases, board membership occurs via an election, with rules that are specified in the bylaws of the organization. It is imperative that the group's bylaws be properly adopted and that the procedures outlined in the bylaws are adhered to carefully. Failure to correctly follow the process could result in a challenge to the legitimacy of the process and invalidate actions under state law.

Board Evaluation

The board's prospective members need to be evaluated based on their ability to meet predetermined criteria that have been communicated clearly.

At least annually, the board should conduct a self-review of performance and provide feedback to each of the board members. This should include a checklist of board responsibilities. Evaluation of present board members could include the following:

- Board members must meet the attendance requirement. This is usually a high percentage of all meetings (e.g. 75 percent).

- Board members must come prepared to meet and discuss the agenda items.
- Board members should be evaluated on their expertise. What skill is each specific member asked to contribute? Is the member an expert in business operations, finance, marketing, or law? It is not uncommon for the group's legal counsel to attend board meetings. At least in theory, board meetings can be protected by attorney-client privilege when legal counsel is present.
- Board members must respect the confidentiality of the board's activities. They must also support the decisions of the board outside the boardroom.
- Board members must disclose conflicts of interest.
- Board members must show respect to management and its role to implement board policy.
- Board members must act in a prudent manner, provide fiduciary responsibility, and understand their behavior is representative of the group at all times.

Exhibit 2.1	
Sample Board Member Job Description	
The ABC Medical Practice's Board Member Job Description and Expectations	
Purpose	To advise, govern, oversee policy and direction, and to assist with the leadership and general promotion of the practice so as to support the organization's mission and needs, and to work closely with the administration of the practice in order to achieve its goals.
Number of Members	[Specify the number of members. The typical board is between 5 and 11 members, depending on the size of the practice.]
Major Responsibilities	• Organizational leadership and advisement • Appoint CEO and evaluate performance • Organization of the executive committee officers and committees • Formulation oversight of policies and procedures • Fiduciary responsibility for the organization • Review and adoption of budget for the organization; review of quarterly financial reports; assist administration with budgetary issues as necessary • Oversight of program planning and evaluation • Hiring, evaluation, and compensation of senior administrative staff • Review of organizational and programmatic reports • Promotion of the organization • Strategic planning oversight
Length of Term	[Specify length of term, which may be staggered.]
Meetings & Time Commitment	[Specify the time and location of meetings such as, "The executive committee will meet every other Friday commencing at 7:30 a.m., and meetings will typically last one (1) hour (this may need to be revised)." An alternative would be to have monthly meetings (2 to 3 hours) in the afternoon or evening (consider payment to participants).]

Exhibit 2.1	
Sample Board Member Job Description *(continued)*	
The ABC Medical Practice's Board Member Job Description and Expectations	
Expectation of ***Board Members***	• Attend and participate in meetings on a regular basis and special events as possible • Participate in standing committees of the board and serve on ad hoc committees, as necessary • Help communicate and promote mission and programs of the practice • Become familiar with the finances and resources of the practice as well as financial and resource needs • Understand the policies and procedures of the practice
Board and Committee Structure	
Establishing Committees	It shall be the responsibility of the executive committee to establish ad hoc and permanent standing committees as necessary to assist in the functioning of the practice. Whenever possible, these committees should contain a representative of the executive committee to provide a proper liaison as well as an administrative staff person.
Typical Committees	May include: finance, personnel, marketing, quality care, and technology. In areas where managed care risk contracting is a significant part of the business environment, a utilization management committee would be common to oversee the risk management of these contracts.

Selection Process

Medical groups are beginning to behave more like traditional business corporations. As part of this change, groups are adding outside persons to the board to improve the governance process and to bring in new ideas and perspectives. These individuals must be

31

chosen carefully with consideration of a number of important criteria, including:

- A general understanding of the region, its business climate, political environment, and some of the key community drivers, as well as some perspective on health care and what is happening in the broad view
- Strategic thinking
- Willingness and ability to attend meetings
- Ability to treat information discreetly
- Some experience as a member of a board
- No conflicts of interest or the appearance of such conflicts (e.g., not someone seeking to do business with the clinic)
- General business acumen
- Contributing without dominating the board
- A history of working well in a group setting (i.e., a "good fit")
- Willingness to sign a confidentiality or nondisclosure agreement
- Willingness to accept fair compensation if applicable

Although many not-for-profit healthcare organizations do not pay their board members, the trend in the healthcare industry is to offer compensation, which can vary according to the size of the organization. Some large hospitals might pay board members as much as $20,000 annually for attending monthly meetings, while others offer much smaller amounts. In general, though, healthcare organizations are recognizing that it is acceptable and fair to offer some compensation in order to attract highly qualified and motivated board members.

Response to Stakeholders' Needs

The medical group's board must deal with a number of stakeholders in the quest to provide effective governance of the group. Some of these stakeholders are:

- Physicians in the medical group practice
- Other physicians in the community

- Employees
- Patients, their families, and caregivers
- Payers
- Government agencies at the federal, state, and local levels
- Hospitals and other healthcare entities
- The community at large

Management of Board Meetings

Most board meetings are governed by *Robert's Rules of Order*,[1] which is the most widely accepted set of procedures for conducting business. These rules are extensive and cover a number of procedures that apply to the medical group setting. Some, however, may not apply to every group's needs, although familiarity with *Robert's Rules* as a whole is important. Whatever system of rules the board decides to adopt, the goal is to apply the rules consistently.

Committee Structure

An essential element of governance is the delegation of tasks and duties for the group. The principal governing body may decide, as allowed or even required by the group's bylaws, to develop a committee structure that addresses operational concerns and processes within the practice in conjunction with the administration. This is a great way to provide physician input in a structured manner instead of on an ad hoc basis. It also provides a great opportunity to develop future leaders by educating them in the committee process.

Some of the more common committees within the governance structure are:

- Executive
- Finance
- Personnel
- Technology
- Quality review
- Management (usually in smaller groups)
- Research

- Recruiting
- Continuing education
- Managed care
- Strategic planning
- Medical practice development (i.e., growth)
- Operational performance
- Ad hoc committees for many purposes, such as new construction, service-line development, patient satisfaction, and contract review

Creating an Executive Committee in a Medical Practice

Going through the process of creating the executive committee must include approval from a majority of stakeholders. It is doubtful that this type of change will be unanimous, although that is certainly preferred. Even though the concept is formally approved, board members will look for ways to revert back to the old form of governance. The executive committee should be consistent and firm and remind the board that this change was approved by the shareholders and there is an expectation of support.

Building effective physician leadership is a work in process. It is helpful to encourage the physicians and administrator to attend joint conferences on management and leadership subjects with expenses being paid by the medical practice. In addition, there are conferences specifically focusing on physicians in leadership roles, which will also be beneficial in building a strong physician-administrator team. The strength of the executive committee will help the board govern the medical practice effectively.

Executive committee responsibilities include operational, financial, and board-assigned tasks, as well as preparing the agenda for and running board meetings.

Daily Operational Issues

Daily operational issues can be dealt with in the following ways:

- The administrator will keep the executive committee informed about personnel, financial, or operational issues.

- Decisions regarding these issues shall be made by the executive committee, administrator, or brought to the board as appropriate.
- The administrator or the executive committee may establish ad hoc committees for special projects, such as recruiting.

Financial Health

The executive committee oversees the financial health of the medical group practice by:

- Focusing on financial opportunities for the medical practice (both revenue enhancement and cost reduction)
- Approving annual operating and capital budgets
- Overseeing compensation plans and benefits
- Monitoring retirement plans, such as 401(k) and performance
- Assessing and recommending investments in new programs and services
- Developing and managing debt strategy
- Recommending the timing and amount of quarterly shareholder bonuses to the board of directors

Tasks Assigned by the Board

The executive committee carries out any tasks assigned to it by the board by gathering information and providing complete analyses on board-referred projects.

Focus of Group Activities

Governing needs to be concerned with the focus of group activities. Activities need to be grouped with consideration for function and customer interaction. In addition, leadership must be empowered to implement and act upon the governing board's policies and decisions. Typically, this would mean the group should focus on three areas of oversight:

1. Internal functions

2. External functions

3. Operations

Regular reports to the board, as well as benchmarking these activities, can be very useful for the effective governance of the organization. It is also important to understand how these activities interact. This interaction has to be governed carefully to prevent a *silo mindset* or *group think* from emerging.

The Executive Officer

Outside of the governing board, the top leader of any medical practice or healthcare organization is the executive officer. The purpose of the executive officer is to ensure the practice or organization operates efficiently, employees have the resources they need, and to ensure quality of care to patients. In short, the executive officer works to ensure the needs of the organization and its patients are met. Additionally, the executive officer provides:

- Leadership
- Support
- Representation
- Organization

Selecting Executive Personnel

Today, there is an increasing demand for healthcare executives and a decreasing pool of qualified candidates. This is primarily due to the number of healthcare networks and large corporate entities that require more leadership at higher levels. In order to compete with larger entities, smaller practices will need to make sure they are providing competitive career opportunities. In some cases, practices may need to hire a professional and provide him or her with education and additional experiences needed to become the executive the practice needs. The practice may wish to hire a professional recruiting firm for the top executive positions. Recruiting firms often have a wider range of candidates to choose from, can advertise more effectively, and have the experience to vet applications.

Whether using a recruiting firm or not, the practice should consider the following when searching for an executive:

- The candidate's education
- The candidate's career experience
- The candidate's professional skills

Organization of the Executive Office

Responsibilities of Executive Officers

Executive officers should have a thorough knowledge and experience in the healthcare environment. Although unique in many ways, health care is still a business and executives must be familiar with finance, marketing, and public relations. It is important that healthcare executives understand office politics among providers, staff, health plans, hospitals, and the community. Communication skills can make or break a healthcare executive. It takes talent and skill to be the liaison between the governing board, employees, and community.

It is every employee's responsibility to ensure clinic compliance with federal, state, and local regulations. It is the executive who will be held responsible by the governing board, but also the name on record for the regulating agencies. Executives must be skilled at determining the strategy of the organization and ensuring that the mission acts as the beacon for decision making and business processes and outcomes. It is the combination of these skills that will determine the financial stability of the organization. Providers can administer quality care every day, but it is the systems put in place that will make the business of healthcare cost effective and sustainable.[2]

Some of the above traits may indicate that the executive is the one with all the answers. However, a Harvard Business Review article reported that one of the key skills of any executive is to be able to ask the right questions.[3] In larger organizations, the executive will have staff that will implement the actions to accomplish the goals. In smaller organizations, executives will need to balance between action and leading the strategic initiatives. Regardless of the size of the organization, the communication of the strategy and leadership to fulfill the mission will be the most essential skills needed for this position.[4]

Measures of Executive Performance

There is a common misconception that once an executive reaches the top level that performance reviews are no longer necessary, other than completing the annual compensation package. However, human behavior can still be refined regardless of the position on the career ladder. Executives should be life-long learners. It is the board's responsibility to provide such refinement through regular feedback sessions. Each year, the Harvard Business Review releases a list of the top 100 CEOs. Over the years, performance measures have evolved to include metrics beyond just finances, and also include relationships with employees, customers, suppliers and their communities. Graham Kenny says, "measuring performance is measuring relationships."[5]

Outcomes Performance Measures

The executive should work with the board of directors to define operating metrics to be used to evaluate the business health of the practice. Basic metrics would include practice growth, profits, productivity, staff retention rate, and patient satisfaction. The strategy should be defined and then reviewed to determine the effectiveness of the implementation. These key performance measurements should be written in objective terms and be specific, measurable, achievable, relevant, and time bound (SMART). These performance measures will be evident by the data and outcomes. The expectations should be clearly identified and defined prior to the review.

Other Performance Measures

More subjective measurements will include evidence of relationships with people both internally and externally. It is important for board members to speak with staff, patients, suppliers and community members to get a sense of the relationship skills that the executive demonstrates. Many practices have failed not because the finances were at risk, but because staff, patients, and community members did not have a good experience with the practice. The problems could be anything from lack of leadership to systems that prevent patients from being seen in a timely manner to the clinic furniture looking dated or worn. All of these issues fall under the scope of executive leadership. Therefore, the board of directors should hold the executive accountable for such relationships and perspectives.

The Process of Evaluating Executives

Just as employees should have regular feedback sessions with leadership, so should the board provide feedback to the executive. Although executive leadership should provide frequent feedback sessions, it is reasonable for the board to only provide feedback sessions twice per year, with one of those being the formal annual performance review. The review should be provided in a planned and private discussion. In most cases, a board subcommittee is responsible for conducting the review with the chair providing the formal feedback. Reviews should include both the strengths and weaknesses, with a plan of expectations set forth for personal development for the next review period. Some organizations want a self-evaluation completed as well and then a plan would be developed to bridge the gap. It should be an expectation that a healthcare executive will provide a professional development goal every year. The stronger the leader, the stronger the organization will be as a whole.

Corporate Record-Keeping

Corporate records are legal documents that must be maintained in accordance with pertinent state and federal laws and regulations, which may vary by state and jurisdiction. Accordingly, it is essential that the governance plan address retention, storage, and retrieval policies for business documents.

The primary responsibility for ensuring proper storage and retention should include a designated backup custodian if the process owner (e.g., the healthcare executive or physician owner or partner) is unavailable. The plan should also include a loss control process for electronic backup of important documents, such as partnership and shareholder agreements, employment contracts, equipment leases, and real estate records. Under most circumstances, it is prudent to retain a copy of important documents at a location physically distant from the primary storage location. This should prevent any type of disaster from destroying executed copies of significant information. Many organizations keep original documents for the length of the statute of limitations pertinent to the most likely allegations related to the document. Some records are evergreen, whereas others may be replaced by newer versions.

The types of documents that should be addressed in a governance plan include, but are not limited to, the following:

Articles of incorporation. In addition to copies retained by the organization and the state of incorporation, a copy should be retained by corporate counsel.

Bylaws. Original and current copies should be retained.

Bylaw changes and documentation. A copy of previous versions of bylaws should be retained for documentation in case of litigation. In addition, it is prudent to keep redlined versions of approved changes to facilitate the tracking of changes.

Stock and/or outstanding shares.

Minutes (board, committee).

Employment agreements (physician, administrator, others). These should be retained in accordance with applicable statutes.

General ledger. Copies of the general ledger should be kept in accordance with applicable tax laws. External accountants or auditors often maintain duplicate records.

Corporate history. Records of corporate history should be retained indefinitely in some retrievable format.

Medical records. Different regulations and statutes apply to the retention of patient medical, employee health, and Occupational Safety and Health Administration records. Patient medical records are generally retained in accordance with the statute of limitations for billing compliance and for bringing malpractice action defined by the individual state or payer contracts. Employee records must be retained in accordance with the type of employee health services and surveillance provided on site. For both types of records, the medical practice should confer with counsel familiar with the applicable statutes for record retention.

Physician credentials. Physician credentialing records may be accessed, despite their presumed protection from discoverability, by a variety of sources: government entities; the Joint Commission; the physician, if ever denied privileges; or a plaintiff who may allege negligent credentialing. Given those potentialities, credentialing records should be maintained for the maximum duration of the statute of limitations for bringing action against the hospital or according to record retention statutes of the state, whichever is longer.[6]

National Practitioner Data Bank (NPDB). NPDB queries and reports should be maintained with and for as long as other credentialing files. Litigation based on negligent credentialing and hiring, or alternatively, litigation alleging wrongful termination or denial of privileges that call into question reports to or from the NPDB, will likely be needed if claims for wrongful termination or negligent credentialing practices are filed.

Discovery documents on current litigation. These documents are important throughout the litigation and appeals process. It is generally practical to retain records for 7 to 10 years after litigation in the event that a related case emerges. Records will likely be retained by counsel, and extended retention may not be required if the records become part of court records submitted as evidence in a trial or court proceeding.

Keeping an Organizational History

Organizational culture is an extremely important aspect of medical practice governance. Of course, positive cultures need to be maintained, and any negative culture needs to be converted to a more positive one. Culture can be maintained by a focus on those aspects that are desirable. Recording the history of the group can enhance positive culture maintenance and make its accomplishments known. Publishing the history of the group in newsletters and websites can help instill pride throughout the organization and maintain a positive culture.

Cultural icons, such as photographs, awards, news articles, and mementos that are symbolic of important events in the group's history, should be properly archived and/or displayed. Activities such as service awards emphasize the group's positive values, which reinforces the importance of such ideals to new employees and physicians.

By its very nature, tribal knowledge is passed between stakeholders by storytelling and relaying the group's mythology to younger members. This information points to what is meaningful to its members, not necessarily to archivists. Be careful to identify and remember the stories that roam the hallways. A great amount of value may be assigned to these traditions and history that we celebrate and share, and they need to be recognized and remembered.

Bylaws

Like policies and procedures, bylaws are dynamic documents that require regular maintenance. Changes in corporate law may require amendments to the bylaws, so a general review of corporate documents should be completed at least annually with special attention being paid to those areas that may have been the subject of changes during the year.

The following questions should be considered as the bylaws and policies of the group are reviewed:

- Has the group changed any committee structures this year?
- Has the group changed any of its procedures on elections?
- Has the group added any new shareholders or have any departed? If so, was their stock exchanged according to the bylaws?

- Are the duties outlined for officers and directors still current?
- Are minutes of meetings recorded and was a quorum present when decisions were made?
- Were the key decisions made according to the bylaws and governance documents?
- Does the group do things differently today than it did in the past?
- Has the makeup of the governance changed enough to warrant reviewing a change to the bylaws?
- Has state corporate law changed since the group's bylaws were last reviewed by legal counsel?

Administrators must protect the integrity of the bylaws because failure to act within the scope of the bylaws may cause legal action by aggrieved shareholders and unnecessary intergroup relationship concerns. It is wise to periodically review the requirements of the bylaws with the board, so the board members fully understand the requirements. It is essential that new board members be oriented to understand this material, and all applicable stakeholders must have access to the governance documents for reference.

Conclusion

Adopting a legal business structure that supports the organization's mission, vision, values, and goals is critical in determining how well a practice will fulfill its mission and achieve its goals.

There are a variety of models available to structure a medical practice, each with its own set of advantages and disadvantages from tax, regulatory and governance perspectives. While selecting the best structure for a practice is often a healthcare executive's responsibility, seeking appropriate legal advice is critically important prior to making a final decision.

The governing board and executives in a practice are key leaders that are essential for ensuring the practice will accomplish its goals and mission.

Notes

1. Robert, Henry M., *Robert's Rules of Order Revised* (Glenview, IL: Scott, Foresman, 1994).

2. "Executive Job Descriptions." MGMA, http://mgma.com.carrer-pathways/for-employers/job-descriptions/executive-job-descriptions, 2020.

3. Allen, J., "How the Best CEOs Get the Important Work Done." *Harvard Business Review*, 2016.

4. Ibid.

5. Kenny, G., "Create KPIs that reflect your strategic priorities." *Harvard Business Review*, Feb. 2020.

6. K.S. Davis, J.C. McConnell, and E.D. Shaw, "Data Management," in *The Risk Management Handbook for Healthcare Organizations*, ed. R. Carroll (San Francisco: Jossey-Bass, 2004), 1220.

Chapter 3

Organizational Governance

Organizational policies and procedures standardize practice operations. They are essential in providing clarity when dealing with issues that are critical to practice operations (e.g., human resources, operations, health and safety protocols, legal liabilities, and regulatory compliance).

Policies and procedures often are discussed together; however, they are not the same or equal. Policies are thought of as an overview, the information that helps staff make decisions. Policies provide guidance. Procedures are the various processes and steps that explain how to execute the policy. Put another way, policies are the overarching viewpoint of the organization and procedures set the policy in motion.

Policies and procedures should be written specifically enough to provide guidance and set organizational expectations, but broadly enough to provide managerial flexibility. A well-written and documented policy or procedure assists in compliance from a regulatory and legal perspective. Policies, since they are broader, will change infrequently, while procedures could change within months of finalizing or after staff members receive training.

Training staff so they know the practice's policies and procedures can be a cumbersome task. In previous years, policies and procedures were printed, three-hole punched, and distributed to each station, office, and cubicle of the practice. As technology became more accessible this routine has changed. This is not to say some policies and procedures aren't printed, but printing them is not ideal in today's environment of constant change and easily accessible electronic documents. The key to policies and procedures is to have employees read them, familiarize themselves with them, and actually use them in their daily work life. The key is not to have them sit unopened on a bookcase, but rather to have employees utilize them to improve patient care, staff engagement, and practice management in general. Consider publishing them electronically on a shared network or portal if it is accessible to all staff members. These documents should be set up with a "view only" status so employees cannot (without your knowledge) adjust or change the policy to suit their needs, or accidentally make changes. Staff must be informed about where and how these policies can be accessed. In addition, policies and procedures should not be made accessible to staff members off-site or after hours.

Written Policies and Procedures

Written policies and procedures establish a standardized practice to reduce variation. If a policy and the procedure for executing it is accurate, helpful, and truly provides clear instructions, this naturally creates a more efficient and evolved workplace. Due to its very nature of explanation and information, it will set staff expectations. These documents serve as a resource for staff, particularly new staff, and create accountability for all. Well-written policies and procedures that are easily accessible also level the playing field for all staff members by reducing the necessity to remember all of the details of each policy and procedure.

Moreover, policy and procedure manuals serve as communication tools with your employees and leadership team. When a particular policy or procedure is not documented well, it will be realized quickly and can be adjusted. These overviews and directives are the unified place your employees can go to gain knowledge, information, and direction.

These policies and procedures, in whatever format they are shared, help to create compliance in a variety of ways. The explanation of how the practice sees the policy, and clarifies its execution through the procedure provides an interpretation of the rules and requirements. This helps the employee understand both the policy and the importance of following the procedure. Multiple policies or procedures may intersect and work together as a unit to meet the requirements of different regulatory and accreditation bodies. This is a double-edged sword, though, if the policies and procedures are not well-written or defined, or if the information is incorrect or inaccurate. This can lead to problems with regulatory and accreditation agencies. It is important to regularly review all policy and procedure manuals, and keep them updated as necessary or appropriate.

Elements of a Policy

Before any part of these documents is drafted, appropriate and relevant research must be conducted. If a committee or small group is drafting the policy, that group should be prepared to defend their viewpoint and research. Those who will utilize the policy or procedure should be consulted with and take part on the committee to ensure accuracy and efficacy. The committee should confirm that all regulatory information is up to date and applicable.

The writing of policies may prove difficult and challenging for some, while others may have very clear viewpoints and communication styles. The key to writing a strong policy and procedure is to be clear and direct. There is no need for flowery language or an overabundance of descriptive words or prose. Policies should be clear-cut written documents that relay the necessary information to all staff members who need it.

Once the documents are drafted, have the appropriate user groups vet the information for suitability and relevance. The healthcare executive should invite other leaders in the practice to review them, as well as in some cases an outside consultant or legal representative. At the very least, the practice compliance officer should always review and approve policies and procedures to make sure they comply.

The elements of a well written policy and procedure include but are not limited to the items below:

- Effective date, version, revision dates
- Title
- Purpose and scope
- Applicability
- Organizational goal(s)
- Definitions or glossary
- Duties of providers and staff – who is involved
- Operational procedures and detailed process
- Related policies or resources
- Policy review period
- Approvals
- Disclaimer that the policy and procedure may be revised without notice

Recommended Policies and Procedures

The medical practice should have policies and procedures that accurately reflect the work completed in the practice. Depending on size, coordinate the policies and procedures based on work product, department or overarching goals.

The departments most likely to have their own policy manuals are:

1. Billing and Receivables
   - Contracted services
   - In-house services
   - Timeframes
   - Training

2. Human Resources
   - Background checks
   - Conflict resolution
   - Drug screening
   - Education
   - Grievance procedure
   - Harassment prevention
   - Health examinations

- Hiring
- Immigration policy and I-9s
- Legal compliance
- Licensure
- Onboarding and orientation
- Performance evaluations
- Skills assessment
- Training

3. Patient Care

- Complaint procedure
- Legal compliance
- Patient dumping
- Philosophy
- Standard of care
- Surveys

4. Inventory Management

- Assessment
- Bids
- Logistics
- Procurement
- Review periods
- Stock levels and fulfillment
- Types

5. Maintenance

- Contracted services
- Equipment maintenance
- Preventive maintenance
- Repair schedules

6. Operations including front office and back office

- Customer service
- Scheduling
- Training

7. Physician practice

- Auxiliary staff
- Bonus programs
- Credentialing
- Hospital programs
- Peer review
- Recruitment
- Travel programs

8. Safety

- Drills
- Injury and illness prevention plans
- Licensure required for staff
- Safety protocols

Conclusion

The goal of clear cut policies and procedures is to communicate how the practice operates and to ensure compliance with all federal, state, and local regulations. The responsibilities and expectations of employees should be given clearly so each staff member understands them. This allows employees to grasp how policies and procedures relate to their jobs, healthcare outcomes, and how to approach their individual tasks as well as a team's tasks. The policies and procedures are the only way for governing agencies to view the practice objectively. Well-documented, well-written, and up-to-date policies and procedures that are accessible to all employees is fundamental to the success of a medical practice.

Index

Page numbers in **bold** reference exhibits and figures.

More from MGMA

The vision of MGMA is "inspiring healthcare excellence for a healthier world." To that end, MGMA is constantly creating and curating resources for medical practice professionals. From podcasts and analysis from the nation's leading experts to tools and interactive webinars to keep you sharp and productive, MGMA has the knowledge you need.

Below is a partial list of what you will find at mgma.com and mgma.com/store.

- **Online Education**
  - MGMA Ed
  - Webinars/Seminars
- **MGMA Data**
  - MGMA DataDive
  - Research & Analysis
  - MGMA *Stat*
- **Website Resources & Tools**
  - Certification and Fellowship
  - MGMA Career Center
  - MGMA Member Community
- **MGMA Government Affairs**
  - *Washington Connection*
- ***MGMA Connection* Magazine**
- **MGMA Podcasts**
  - Insights
  - Executive Session
- **MGMA Consulting**
- **Continuing Education**
- **Books**
- **Insight Articles, Member Tools, Case Studies, and More!**

Remember: Be sure to visit mgma.com/BOKupdates to keep up with all updates to the *Body of Knowledge Review Series, 4th Edition.*

Printed in the USA
CPSIA information can be obtained
at www.ICGtesting.com
JSHW011110211223
54061JS00011B/143